MOM & me

from you to me®

MOM & Me

Mom & Me will take you on an interactive and fun journey, having a great time getting to know each other better.

Tips to enjoy Mom & Me :

- Your questions are in green. Mom's questions are in purple.

- Dip in and complete your questions in any order, whenever you want.

- Use words, drawings, doodles ... whatever feels right for you.

- There are no right or wrong answers, just your own.

- Use the extra pages to capture anything else you would like to explore.

- Agree when and how to share your pages with the other person.

- Enjoy yourself and have fun!

A bit about Mom . . .

My full name :

My age :   Today's Date :

A picture of Mom . . . a drawing or photo

MOM

A bit about Me . . .

My full name :

My age :   Today's date :

A picture of Me . . . a drawing or photo

Me

A bit about Mom . . .

What I love watching on television :

Best movies :

Top Songs :

Favorite places :

Things I Say a lot :

I love to eat :

MOM

A bit about Me . . . .

What I love watching on television :

Best movies :

Top songs :

Favorite places :

Things I say a lot :

I love to eat :

Me

Today . . .

Who I talked to :

What I did :

The best things :

The worst things :

What I wanted to do, but didn't get around to :

MOM

Today . . .

Who I talked to :

What I did :

The best things :

The worst things :

What I wanted to do, but didn't get around to :

Me

When I was younger . . .

My earliest memory :

What I was like :

When I was younger I thought that :

MOM

When I was younger . . .

My earliest memory :

What I was like :

When I was younger I thought that :

Me

Happened to me . . .

Funny things :

Embarrassing things :

Sad things :

MOM

Happened to me . . .

Funny things :

Embarrassing things :

Sad things :

Me

The way we are . . .

The ways we are Similar :

The ways we are different :

Things I admire about you :

MOM

The way we are . . . .

The ways we are similar :

The ways we are different :

Things I admire about you :

Me

My family . . .

Some great memories of our family :

What I love about our family :

What I would like to be different :

MOM

My family . . .

Some great memories of our family :

What I love about our family :

What I would like to be different :

Me

Family times . . .

Things I love doing with my family :

I wish we could :

I wish we didn't :

MOM

Family times . . .

Things I love doing with my family :

I wish we could :

I wish we didn't :

Me

Where I live . . .

What I remember about the places I have lived :

Things at home that are special :

Where I might like to live in the future :

MOM

Where I live . . .

What I remember about the places I have lived :

Things at home that are special :

Where I might like to live in the future :

Me

Birthdays . . .

My best memories :

How I would like to spend future birthdays :

My perfect present would be :

MOM

Birthdays . . .

My best memories :

How I would like to spend future birthdays :

My perfect present would be :

Me

Vacations . . .

My best memories :

The best places I have been :

Where I would love to visit :

MOM

Vacations . . .

My best memories :

The best places I have been :

Where I would love to visit :

Me

With friends . . .

How I feel about my friends :

What I admire most about you and your friends :

What I want to change about my friendships :

MOM

With friends . . .

How I feel about my friends :

What I admire most about you and your friends :

What I want to change about my friendships :

Me

Messages for my friends . . .

To:

To:

To:

To:

To:

To:

MOM

Messages for my friends . . .

To:

To:

To:

To:

To:

To:

Me

My Spare time . . .

What I enjoy doing most in my spare time :

What I would love to do :

What I love watching you do :

MOM

My spare time . . . .

what I enjoy doing most in my spare time :

what I would love to do :

what I love you watching me do :

Me

School . . .

what I loved about being at school :

what I found most difficult :

with the benefit of hindsight :

MOM

School . . .

What I love about being at school :

What I find most difficult :

My greatest learning experience :

Me

Learning . . .

What I would love to learn :

How I best like to learn :

The help I would like from you :

MOM

Learning . . .

What I would love to learn :

How I best like to learn :

The help I would like from you :

Me

Books & stories . . .

Some of my favorite books :

Books I love that I hope you will read :

Books I would love to read :

Books & stories . . .

Some of my favorite books :

Favorite characters from my books :

Books I would love to read :

Me

Some of my favorite things . . .

MOM

Some of my favorite things . . .

Me

Growing up . . .

What was exciting :

What I was concerned about :

The help and guidance I received :

MOM

Growing up . . .

What is exciting :

What I am concerned about :

The help I would like :

Me

My body . . .

How I feel about me :

What I like about me :

What I would like to share with you :

MOM

My body . . .

How I feel about me :

What I like about me :

What I would like to share with you :

Me

Being healthy . . .

A drawing of my ideas to be fit and healthy :

MOM

Being healthy . . .

A drawing of my ideas to be fit and healthy :

Me

Feeling happy . . .

The things that make me happy :

What makes me feel confident :

Who I love spending time with :

MOM

Feeling happy . . .

The things that make me happy :

What makes me feel confident :

Who I love spending time with :

Me

Feeling Sad . . .

The things that make me sad :

What shakes my confidence :

What helps me when I feel sad :

MOM

Feeling sad . . .

The things that make me sad :

What shakes my confidence :

What helps me when I feel sad :

Me

My worries . . .

Things that worry me :

Some of my regrets :

How I best manage any worries :

MOM

My worries . . .

Things that worry me :

Some of my regrets :

How I best manage any worries :

Me

Falling in love . . .

My views on love :

What is important to me :

My first love and what I learned :

MOM

Falling in love . . .

My views on love :

What is important to me :

What I have learnt so far :

Me

My future . . .

Things I want to do in my life :

Things I want to do with you :

Some words to describe the person I want to be :

MOM

My future . . .

Things I want to do in my life :

Things I want to do with you :

Some words to describe the person I want to be :

Me

My dreams . . .

What I dream about :

How I see my future :

What I wish I could spend more time doing :

MOM

My dreams . . .

What I dream about :

How I see my future :

What I wish I could spend more time doing :

Me

Mom & Me . . .

What I love about you :

What I love about us :

What I wish we could do more of :

MOM

Me & Mom . . .

What I love about you :

What I love about us :

What I wish we could do more of :

Me

Thoughts I have . . .

In 5 years :

I hope :

Something you don't know about me :

MOM

Thoughts I have . . . .

In 5 years :

I hope :

Something you don't know about me :

Me

Helping others . . .

People I admire who help others :

How I like to help others :

What I could do more :

MOM

Helping others . . .

People I admire who help others :

How I like to help others :

What I could do more :

Me

Topics of Mom's choice . . .

These pages are for you, Mom, to write questions . . .

MOM

Topics of Mom's choice . . .

. . . or topics for you and your child to answer

Me

Topics of my choice . . . .

These pages are for you to write questions . . .

MOM

Topics of my choice . . .

. . . or topics for you and your Mom to answer

Me

A poem about me & you . . .

MOM

A poem about me & you . . .

Me

A letter to myself based on what I have discovered in this journal . . .

Dear Me

MOM

A letter to myself based on what I
have discovered in this journal . . .

Dear Me

Me

Thinking about what I have discovered
from this journal, here is a picture
showing my dreams for the future . . .

MOM

Thinking about what I have discovered from this journal, here is a picture showing my dreams for the future . . .

Me

Final thoughts & doodles . . .

MOM

Final thoughts & doodles . . .

Me

MOM &me

First published in the USA by *from you to me* February 2015.

Copyright from you to me limited 2015

ISBN 978-1-907048-66–1

Printed and bound in China by Imago.

This paper is manufactured from pulp sourced from forests that are legally and sustainably managed.

For more information please contact:

from you to me ltd

The Old Brewery

Newtown

Bradford on Avon

BA15 1NF, UK

hello@fromyoutome.com

www.fromyoutome.com

Published by *from you to me* ltd

All titles are available at good gift and book stores or www.fromyoutome.com

from you to me Journals of a Lifetime
Dear Mom
Dear Dad
Dear Grandma
Dear Grandpa
Dear Sister
Dear Brother
Dear Daughter
Dear Son
Dear Friend

Parent & Child
Bump to Birthday, pregnancy & first year journal
Our Story, for my daughter
Our Story, for my son
Dear Baby, guest book
Early Years, birth to five years journal

Get Kids Writing
Mom & Me
Dad & Me
Grandma & Me
Grandpa & Me

Other Titles
Love Stories, anniversary & relationship journal
Cooking up Memories

Many of these journals can be personalized online at www.fromyoutome.com

from you to me ®